SEVEN SILLY WISE MEN

SEVEN
SILLY
WISE MEN

By James Cloyd Bowman

and Margery Bianco

From a Translation by

Aili Kolehmainen

Pictures by John Faulkner

ALBERT WHITMAN & Company, Chicago

Text © 1936, 1964 by Albert Whitman & Company
Illustrations © 1965 by Albert Whitman & Company
L.C. Catalog Card 65-15102
Published simultaneously in Canada by George J. McLeod, Ltd., Toronto
Lithographed in the United States of America

Foreword

The world round there have always been fools, num-skulls, and nitwits known at different times and places as sillies, morons, or noodles. Wherever their home, the nonsense they contrive makes good telling.

Often the people of one part of a country tell with gusto about fellow countrymen known for their peculiar ways. Thus in England there are droll stories about the men of Gotham, in Switzerland it is the townsmen of Meiringen, while in the United States the backwoods-man exercises his own peculiar logic, sometimes at the expense of the outsider who laughed.

Thus the wise men of Holmola may be Finnish, but they belong to the world at large. In one way, however, they illustrate a strand of folklore typical of Finland. This is a belief in the magic of words and spells. The men of Holmola can easily blame their troubles on wizards, but, as you will see, they can do quite well without any help at all.

YEARS AGO, in a far-off corner of Finland, there was a little town called Holmola. The people who lived there were known as the Holmolaiset.

It was not often that a stranger ever went to Holmola. And from living year after year by themselves and never seeing or hearing anything of the outside world, the Holmolaiset grew to be quite different from the rest of the people in Finland, and rather queer in their ways.

They were simpleminded and above all cautious. They liked to turn everything over carefully in their minds before they decided what to do. When it came to any important question, they would talk it over for weeks and months and even years before they could make up their minds to act.

So in time the Holmolaiset grew to be quite famous among the other people of Finland. The few strangers who visited them brought back some very funny stories about their ways.

1

WHEN THE FOLK at Holmola first began to grow rye, they had the greatest trouble in the world deciding how to harvest it. In fact, while they sat around talking and arguing about how the job should be done, their first crop grew ripe and wasted. There were only a few handfuls saved to seed the ground for the second year.

By the time this second crop was ripe, the wise men of the village had thought out a very careful plan. Not a single grain was to be wasted this time. They divided the whole town into crews of seven men each, and each crew set solemnly to work.

The first man bent the rye stalks over, one at a time.

The second man held a piece of wood under each stalk.

The third man cut the stalk with a sharp hatchet.

The fourth man gathered the stalks into sheaves, which the fifth man bound.

The sixth man carried the sheaves away, and the seventh built them into a stack.

All this took so long that most of the crop was lost again—for by working their hardest, seven men together could only harvest two sheaves a day!

A stranger named Matti happened to visit the town
while this great harvesting work was going on. He was
so amazed at what he saw that he decided to teach the
men of Holmola a thing or two. He hurried back to
his own town and returned with a sickle.

That night, while the Holmola men were resting after their enormous labors, Matti went out by moonlight into the rye field. In a very short time he cut and bound more sheaves than all the townsfolk together had been able to harvest in a week. Then he dropped his sickle beside the last sheaf he had bound and went to bed.

In the morning, Matti came out to see what the people would make of it all.

When the Holmola men found their rye all cut and bound and the sickle lying on the ground, they were struck dumb with surprise.

For a week and a day they did nothing but talk it over. At last they decided that all this dangerous work must have been done by magic spells and that the wizard who had done it had afterwards changed himself into the sickle. So now for their own safety they must get rid of the sickle, and the best way to do that would be to drown it.

They all agreed, after much talk, that anyone who touched the sickle or came within an eel's length of it would be taking his life in his hands. So they went to the woods and cut a long pole. They tied a leather noose on the end of the pole, and with this they managed to drag the sickle along the ground.

All the townsfolk came out to watch. Sure enough, that sickle was alive! Didn't it fight every inch of the way not to be drowned? It kept catching at roots and stumps and rocks, at the banks of ditches, and it was with the greatest trouble in the world that at last it was dragged to the edge of the lake.

And then? Then the wise men left it there, while they spent another day standing about and arguing as to how to get the sickle into the water.

Finally they dragged it into a boat and towed it out to the middle of the lake. With another pole and another noose they managed to tie a big rock to the sickle so that it wouldn't float. Then with a shout of triumph they tipped the rock into the water.

But not the sickle. The sickle caught on the edge of the boat, and now they were all in a panic. They were sure the wizard was struggling to the very last gasp. There he hung, clutching at their boat, trying to drown them.

Sure enough, the boat was tipping! The weight of the rock in the water was dragging the boat down. And in another minute, there they all were, spluttering and paddling away for their lives.

But the sickle was drowned. It was safe at the bottom of the lake. The whole town declared a month's holiday to celebrate their escape. Now they could go on in their own ways, as their fathers had done, with no fear of wizards coming to interfere with them.

When Matti went home and told what happened, the news spread like wildfire and all Finland laughed.

2

WHEN MATTI next came to visit the Holmolaiset, he found them all in a great to-do, one arguing against the other. They had been arguing for over a year. And this is how it all began.

For as long as the oldest men of Holmola could remember, the Holmolaiset had always lived in kotas, or houses shaped like wigwams. Lately they had, after much thought, decided to build for themselves tupas, or simple one-room log huts.

They had planned the whole work carefully and divided the townsfolk into work crews.

One man was to cut down the trees, another to trim the boughs, and four others would peel the bark off. The seventh man would measure the tree into lengths, while the eighth and ninth cut it up into logs. Then the next four would carry these logs to the spot where the tupa was to be built. The fourteenth and fifteenth would match the logs at the ends so that they fitted together, and the next four would set them in place for the walls. Later on, others would lay the roof.

The work went slowly, but with no great difficulty. Nothing went wrong till the first tupa was completed.

Then came a great shock.

The wise men of the village had reasoned that the special advantage of the tupa was that it would always be filled with sunshine, summer and winter alike. For they argued that by building the walls and laying the roof while the sun was shining, carefully chinking all the cracks as they went along, the sunshine would be trapped inside the tupa and kept prisoner there forever.

But when their tupas came to be finished, instead of being filled with sunshine inside they were as black as pitch. And this so amazed the wise men after all their planning that they sat down to reason out just how it had happened.

They were all sure that the sunlight couldn't possibly have escaped by itself. Hadn't they walled it in and roofed it down with all the care in the world?

No, someone had gone to work and let the sunlight out again. That was sure. And the only person that could possibly do this must have been a wizard. So they set about getting the sunlight back again by the use of charms and spells.

But the charms didn't work, and the spells didn't work. So they all sat down in front of their kotas to think out another plan.

After months of arguing back and forth they came to an agreement. What they had to do was to carry the sunlight into each tupa. A very simple idea—why hadn't they thought of it sooner?

Again they organized the whole village. The women carded and spun and wove to make great woolen sacks. When they were finished, the men divided into groups. Eight men held each bag open to the sunlight.

When a sack was filled, it was closed and bound tightly before the sunlight could escape. Then the sacks were carried inside the tupas.

But no, this plan didn't work either. The people tried it over and over again, but something seemed to happen to the sunlight each time. So down they sat themselves to think it out, and the longer they argued, the more they disagreed. What happened to the sunlight nobody could make out.

When Matti arrived, he found them all shouting and quarreling, sixteen to the dozen.

He listened to their careful arguments and their tales of woe. Then he said:

"Men of Holmola, I don't pretend to be wiser than anyone else. But in my town we have long ago discovered the secret of the sun. If you'll pay me a thousand marks, I'll show you how to get the sunlight into your tupas."

After much talk the villagers agreed.

"All right," said Matti. "Now watch."

Into the nearest tupa he strode. He took his axe from his belt, hacked out a square hole in the wall, and in streamed the sunlight. It flooded the earthen floor and the wooden benches and the wooden tables with a golden glow.

The villagers were amazed. In fact they were so delighted with this great invention that they decided to improve upon it themselves. They started to hack the whole wall down, shouting as they saw the sunshine pouring in more and more.

The men worked so hard that at last the whole roof came tumbling down on their heads!

After their work had come to nothing, the wise men decided that, all things considered, a kota was a better kind of house than a tupa.

3

WHEN MATTI next visited Holmola, he was surprised to find nearly half the villagers missing. When he asked about it, he was told this story.

It seemed that late in the autumn, a fire had broken out in the brush around the lakeshore and had driven a pack of wolves from cover. The wolves got in among the village cattle grazing on the opposite shore and killed the oldest cow.

One of the herdsmen drove the wolves off before they had time to eat the meat. Then he told the villagers what had happened.

The Holmolaiset rowed across the lake, discussing on their way what was the best thing to do.

The cow was dead. There was no need for any long argument about that. But now that it was dead, what should be done about it?

After many hours of talk, they decided to roast the meat from the cow in front of the brush fire.

They brought the cow back across the lake in their boat, but by this time the fire had nearly burned itself out. All the same, they cut pieces of meat and tried to roast them on sticks before the dying embers.

When they thought the meat was cooked enough and ought to be crisp and brown, they began to eat it. But the meat did not taste good. It was smoky and only half cooked. So they threw it away and sat down to argue about what they should eat instead.

After some days they decided that it might be possible to catch some fish in the lake and cook them to make a meal. Whereupon they got out their nets and dragged the lake, but not a fish could they find.

So once more the villagers sat down to talk it over.

Soon they all agreed that the best thing to eat would be porridge. But by this time, with all their talking and arguing, a hard frost had set in and the lake was covered with thick ice.

The people were very hungry, and they had no kettle big enough to cook all the porridge they wanted to eat. So they had the bright idea of preparing their porridge in the lake.

"We'll cut a big hole in the ice and pour our meal in," they decided, "and then we can all eat our fill."

After more talk, they finally agreed upon the exact size that the hole ought to be. Half a dozen men went out to mark the ice, while others followed with picks to cut out the hole.

Then the cook and his helpers marched out. They began to pour the meal through the opening, stirring the water with a long stick. When they all decided that the porridge should be thick enough to eat, the cook stooped down to taste it and make sure there was no mistake.

But it so happened that the cook slipped on the ice and went headlong through the hole.

The others waited for his return. As time went by
and still he did not appear, they began to argue about
why he stayed down there so long.

"The porridge is so good," said the oldest man, "that
he must be sitting there on the bottom of the lake
stuffing himself, eating all our shares."

"That's so!" cried the others. "There'll be none left
for the rest of us."

One of the villagers volunteered to find the cook
and fetch him back. He went forward very carefully,
but he too slipped at just the wrong moment and went
headlong through the hole.

When neither the cook nor the man returned, the rest grew very angry. After some time a third man went to see what was happening down there. But as he leaned over the hole to shout, he too slipped and down he went.

And so, one by one, they each went to find out what had happened to their friends, until the last man of all had tumbled through the hole.

And for all that Matti could learn, there they still were, sitting on the bottom of the lake, planning and arguing and eating their fill of porridge.

And there they may still be, to this very day.

A Brief Note About Finnish Folklore

This picture book, *Seven Silly Wise Men,* is taken from the author's longer book, *Tales from a Finnish Tupa,* published by Albert Whitman and Company. This volume contains fables and stories of magic as well as droll tales.

Dr. James Cloyd Bowman was among the American scholars who pioneered in collecting material about mythical folk heros such as Paul Bunyan, Mike Fink, John Henry and Pecos Bill. He published stories about each of these larger-than-life men and his interest in folklore enriched his years of college teaching. Margery Bianco, well known for her children's stories, collaborated with Dr. Bowman on his collection of Finnish tales.

In Finland, the scholarly collection of folklore began early in the nineteenth century. Some magic runes and tales were published before this, but the great interest in the Finnish language and its cultural traditions came in the eighteen-hundreds. This interest had a significant part in heightening the feeling of Finnish national unity when Finland was under Russian rule.

The collection of hero tales, the great epic poem known as the *Kalevala,* was published more than a century ago. Today it is estimated that there are well over a million separate items of folk material—tales, songs, runes, riddles, and proverbs—in manuscript collections in Finland.

While Dr. Bowman has pointed out the emphasis on magic words and spells that is typical of Finnish folklore, it is also interesting to see eastern and western European traditions meet in Finland. From Scandinavia to the west come stories of animals and giants; from Russia to the east come tales of princes and princesses. Often purer forms of original stories exist in Finnish manuscripts than are known elsewhere. The Finns, however, have also produced a large body of their own folklore with its own characteristics.

For more than a century Finnish scholars have contributed to the scientific study of folk materials. A widely used classification system was first proposed by a Finnish researcher. As with European folklore in general, it has been possible to trace strands of Finnish tales to ancient India and to Europe of the Middle Ages.